Roary's Big Race

STICKER STORYBOOK

First published in Great Britain by HarperCollins Children's Books in 2008

3 5 7 9 10 8 6 4 2

ISBN 10: 0-00-725523-3

ISBN 13: 978-0-00-725523-8

© Chapman Entertainment Limited & David Jenkins 2008.

Visit Roary at www.roarytheracingcar.com

Printed in Malaysia

It was a very special race day at Silver Hatch. The cars were getting ready to test Farmer Green's new green fuel – made from compost!

"I wonder where Big Chris is," said Roary, "he's not usually late on race day!"

Can you help the cars? See if you can find a sticker of Big Chris and put him in the workshop.

"Here I am," said Big Chris. "I hope you lot are all ready for today's race! I've a feeling it's going to be a really good one today. Tin Top, how's your new fender?"

"Feeling good, thanks, Big Chris. Tin Top's in tiptop condition!"
Tin Top grinned. "But I could do with a bit of a touch up!"

How many words can you find that rhyme with Tin Top?
Write them at the bottom of the page then give Tin Top
a new look with your stickers.

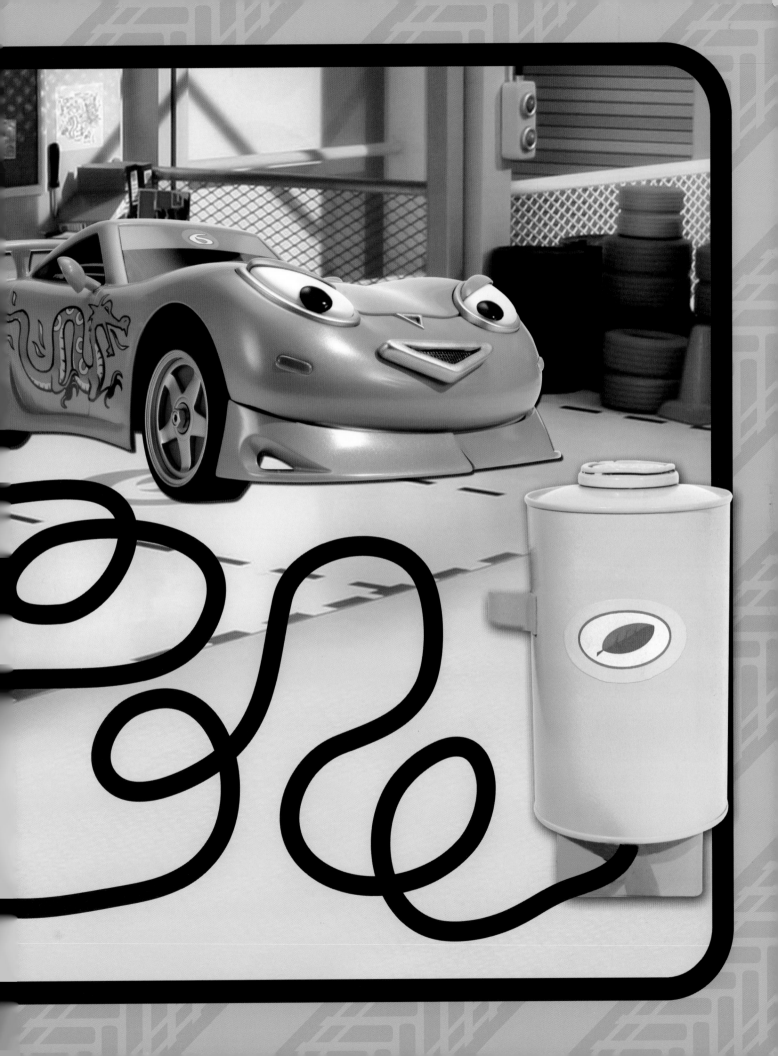

"How about you, Cici?" asked Big Chris.

"I am very excited, Big Chris," said Cici, doing a little hop.

Cici is car number 3. Can you find some stickers with groups of three things to add to the picture? For example, three tyres, or three traffic cones?

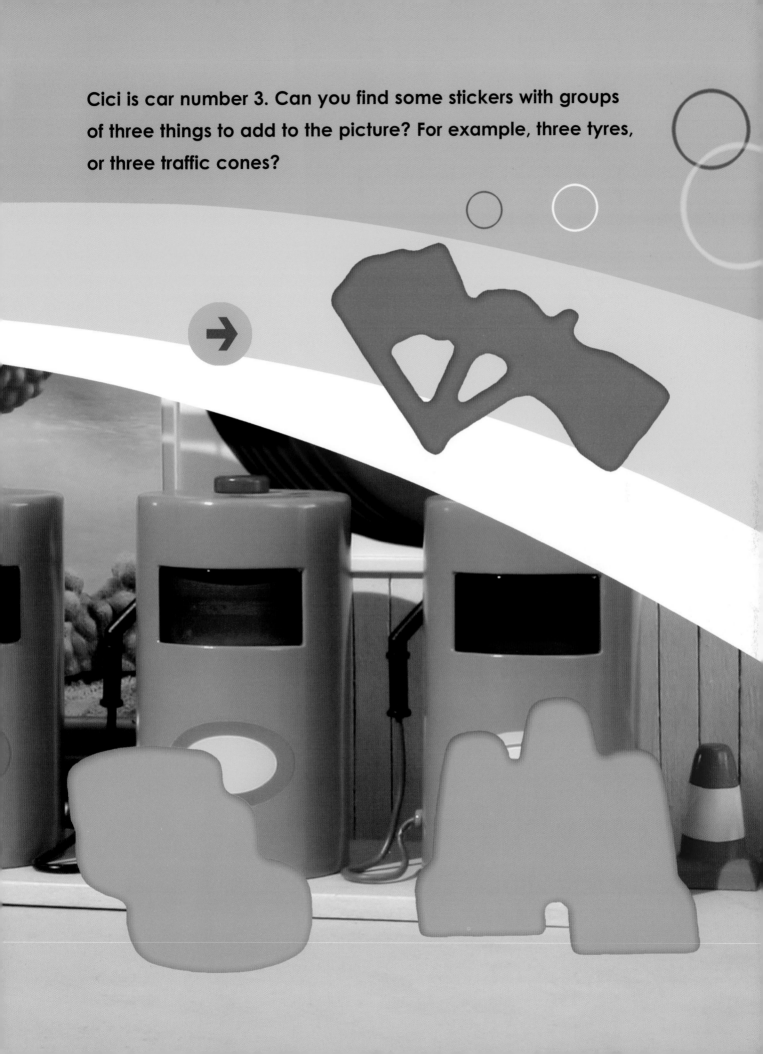

Maxi had overdone it a bit in the practise lap, as usual.

"Maxi, how's your oil?" asked Big Chris.

"It could do with topping up," said Maxi, sulkily.

"Well, we'll soon put that right", said Big Chris. "Now, where's the oil can?

Can you find the oil can? When you find it, put a chequered flag sticker next to it so Big Chris knows where to look!

"Now then, Roary," said Big Chris. "What about you? Are you ready to race?"

"I'm raring to go, Big Chris," said Roary. "All I need is a little top-up of Farmer Green's fuel."

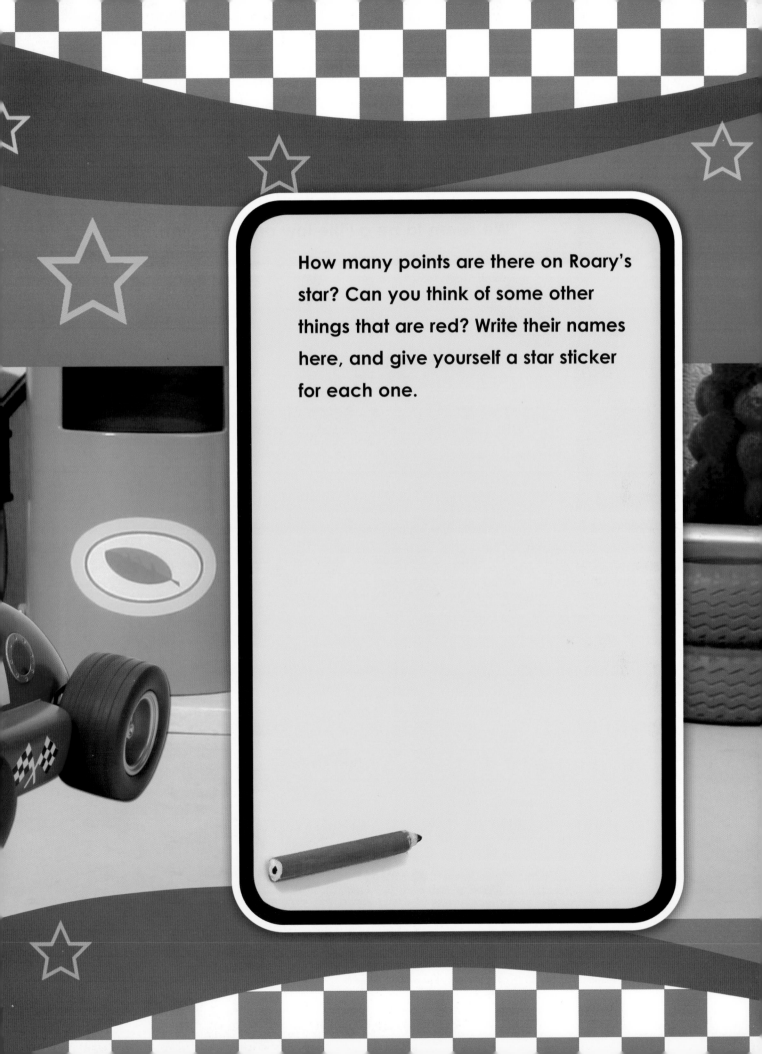

How many points are there on Roary's star? Can you think of some other things that are red? Write their names here, and give yourself a star sticker for each one.

The other cars joined in: "We all need topping up!" they chorused.

"No prob – ah, erm, perhaps there is a problem," said Big Chris, as he looked at the fuel tanks.

"We seem to be a little low on fuel... Erm..."

There are lots of different kinds of fuel, or power, that can drive machines. See if you can find the following words in the wordsearch grid. They can read in all directions.

P	Z	Q	U	J	F	U	E
L	E	P	D	N	I	W	L
R	H	T	D	C	R	G	E
L	P	O	R	C	B	T	C
G	A	S	K	O	H	Y	T
X	Y	R	S	G	L	O	R
B	A	T	T	E	R	Y	I
R	H	J	I	V	F	U	C
L	I	O	I	F	J	O	I
P	G	V	U	G	A	U	T
O	P	C	R	L	U	M	Y
Y	C	S	O	L	A	R	W

Oil   Battery
Coal   Wind
Electricity   Solar
Gas   Petrol

Just then, Marsha arrived. "Are we all ready to race?" she asked. "I'm so excited!"

"Erm, yes, well, nearly, Marsha," Big Chris stammered. "Just got to top up the cars and then we're ready to roll…"

"Great!" said Marsha. "I think today's race is going to be a good one!"

"Oh, dear. What are we going to do now?" asked Big Chris,
looking at the cars.

"I've got enough to get to Farmer Green's and back,"
said Roary. "I'll ask him to bring some more fuel over."

"Thanks, Roary," said Big Chris, sounding relieved.

"You're a star!"

Big Chris has left his spanners lying around all over the place. Can you find them for him? There should be five in total. When you've found them all, put the sticker with Maxi's number five at the bottom of the page.

Off Roary went down the track
to Farmer Green's. "How's things,
Roary?" asked Flash as he
zoomed past Hare-Pin Bend.
"Can't stop, Flash," Roary replied.
"Got to get some fuel!"

How many carrots can you count?
Can you add two more
from the stickers?

Roary sped past Carburettor Corner, where Molecom was surprised to find himself on the wrong side of the barrier. "Hi Roary," Molecom called. "Where am I now?" "Carburettor Corner, Molecom," laughed Roary, as he disappeared from view.

Roary soon arrived at Farmer Green's farm shop, but Farmer Green was nowhere to be seen.

He had already left for the racetrack!

Roary was so disappointed. Now he would have to go back to Big Chris with the bad news. The race would probably have to be cancelled. What a bad day it was turning out to be.

There are lots of green things in this picture – how many can you point out?

Apples
Doors
Shutters
Trees
Grass

But when Roary got back to the track, Big Chris was beaming. Farmer Green had come to watch the race, but he'd brought FB with some fuel!

"I haven't been filled up!" cried Roary.
"Sorry, Roary, there just isn't time now," said Big Chris.

Can you add Roary to the starting grid?

Marsha flagged the cars off and the race began as usual. All the cars ran really well on the new fuel, but Roary was sure he would run out before reaching the finishing line.

Suddenly, Roary realised that he was just behind Maxi, and coming up to the finish line. He made one last effort and whizzed past Maxi to win the race! Not having very much fuel had actually made him faster!

Use the Roary and Maxi stickers to make counters then take turns throwing a die and follow the arrows to move. First to the finish line wins the race!

FINISH

ANSWERS

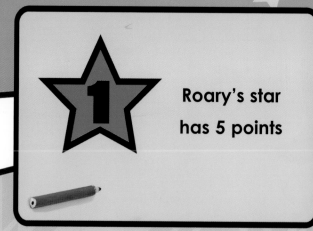

Page 10-11

Page 12-13

Roary's star has 5 points

Page 15

P	Z	Q	U	J	F	U	E
L	E	P	D	N	I	W	L
R	H	T	D	C	R	G	E
L	P	O	R	C	B	T	C
G	A	S	K	O	H	Y	T
X	Y	R	S	G	L	O	R
B	A	T	T	E	R	Y	I
R	H	J	I	V	F	U	C
L	I	O	I	F	J	O	I
P	G	V	U	G	A	U	T
O	P	C	R	L	U	M	Y
Y	C	S	O	L	A	R	W

Page 18-19

Page 20-21